Romeo and Juliet

A SHORTER SHAKESPEARE

Romeo and Juliet

Illustrated by Cal Williams

MACMILLAN • USA

MACMILLAN
A Simon & Schuster Macmillan Company
1633 Broadway
New York, NY 10019

First published in 1996 by
Appletree Press Ltd,
19-21 Alfred Street,
Belfast BT2 8DL.

MACMILLAN is a trademark of Macmillan, Inc.
Library of Congress Cataloging-in-Publication Data
Shakespeare, William, 1564-1616.
  Romeo and Juliet: shorter Shakespeare/William Shakespeare.
  p. cm.
  ISBN 0-02-861228-0
  1. Shakespeare, William, 1564-1616–Adaptations. I. Title.
PR2878.R6 1996
822.3'3–dc20   96-16129
                                                     CIP

Printed in Singapore

10 9 8 7 6 5 4 3 2 1

The action of *Romeo and Juliet* takes place in Italy during the fifteenth century. Italy is a country with a fierce pride in family name and reputation. Family feuds are common, not only between members of the aristocracy but also among their subjects, servants, and tenants. To "belong" to a house does not mean to be directly related to that family but to be "bound" to the family either by blood or affection, or by way of employment or geographical location. This means that a small slight or oversight by a member of one house toward another can lead to a virtual "war."

The Montague and Capulet feud of this play is a typical example of such rivalry. We never learn the origins of the dispute - we are told that it is an "ancient grudge," carried on from generation to generation. It appears that the actual cause is no longer of importance, and that the feud has assumed a life of its own. It seems to be taking over the city of Verona - there are regular fights and riots, often purposely started rather than avoided. The heads of each family seem unable to stop the spread and eruption of hatred.

As we join the play, we meet Sampson and Gregory, two servants of the house of Capulet, who are bragging of what they would do to any man or maid of the house of Montague. They are excited by the drama of the conflict, and their bravado and swaggering reveals their need to prove their loyalty and manliness. As a result they goad two Montague servants they meet into fighting. Their argument is contrived, and it is obvious that they do not believe any of the insults they hurl at their foes but are simply trying to force their rivals to draw first.

This is the backdrop against which our two "star-crossed lovers," Romeo, a Montague, and Juliet, a Capulet, meet and fall in love. The couple are young and idealistic, as yet untouched by their families' bitterness, though they are, naturally, aware of the feud. When each discovers the identity of the other they despair, knowing their love to be forbidden and therefore impossible. While we hope for their success, our introduction to their world has made the pathos of their plight all too clear: at best, Romeo and Juliet risk exile from their families as traitors; at worst, death at the hands of their enemies.

> *Romeo and Juliet was first*
> *performed in 1595.*

Romeo and Juliet

The scene is Verona, Italy, during the fifteenth century. We open on a city street where a crowd has
assembled. The two chief families in Verona - the
Capulets and the Montagues - have long been involved in
a feud that has caused frequent street disturbances and
bloodshed. The situation has become so serious that the
Prince now intervenes with a royal proclamation.

PRINCE: Throw your mistempered weapons to the
            ground,
    And hear the sentence of your moved prince.
    Three civil brawls bred of an airy word,

By thee, old Capulet, and Montague.
Have thrice disturbed the quiet of our streets
And made Verona's ancient citizens
Cast by their grave beseeming ornaments
To wield old partisans in hands as old,
Cankered with peace, to part your cankered hate.
If ever you disturb our streets again,
Your lives shall pay the forfeit of the peace.

Shortly after the incident, Lord Capulet holds a masked ball to which he invites his kinsfolk and all local nobility not of the house of Montague. Despite the danger, Romeo, son of Lord Montague, is persuaded by his cousin Benvolio to attend the feast because Romeo's "beloved," Rosaline, will be there. Unfortunately, Rosaline does not return Romeo's affections and Benvolio hopes to cure his friend Romeo of his unrequited love.

BENVOLIO: At this same ancient feast of Capulet
Sups the fair Rosaline, whom thou so lov'st,
With all the admired beauties of Verona:
Go thither and, with unattainted eye,
Compare her face with some that I shall show
And I will make thee think thy swan a crow.

ROMEO: When the devout religion of mine eye
Maintains such falsehood, then turn tears to fires;
Amid these, who, often drowned, could never die,

Transparent heretics, be burnt for liars.
One fairer than my love! the all-seeing sun
Never saw her match, since first the world begun.

BENVOLIO: Tut! you saw her fair, none else being by
Herself poised with herself in either eye;
But in that crystal scale, let there be weighed
Your lady's love against some other maid,
That I will show you shining at this feast,
And she shall scant show well, that now shows best.

ROMEO: I'll go along, no such sight to be shown,
But to rejoice in splendour of mine own.

Accompanied by Benvolio and a friend, Mercutio,
Romeo sets forth for the ball, though with a troubled
heart, a portent of what is to come.

ROMEO: ... my mind misgives,
Some consequence, yet hanging in the stars,
Shall bitterly begin his fearful date
With this night's revels;

The party arrives at the house and Old Capulet bids
them welcome, not recognizing them as Montagues
because they are all wearing masks. Romeo and his
friends join in the merriment and dancing, when Romeo
is suddenly struck with the beauty of a young lady.

ROMEO: What lady's that which doth enrich the hand
   Of yonder knight?

SERVANT: I know not, sir.

ROMEO: O she doth teach the torches to burn bright.
   It seems she hangs upon the cheek of night,
   As a rich jewel in an Ethiop's ear.
   Beauty too rich for use, for earth too dear!
   So shows a snowy dove trooping with crows,
   As yonder lady over her fellows shows.
   The measure done, I'll watch her place of stand,
   And, touching hers, make blessed my rude hand.
   Did my heart love till now? Forswear it sight,
   For I never saw true beauty till this night.

   Romeo is overheard by Tybalt, a nephew of Lord
Capulet, who knows by the voice that he who speaks is
Romeo of the family Montague, enemy of the Capulets.

TYBALT: This, by his voice should be a Montague. -
   Fetch me my rapier, boy. - What! dares the slave
   Come hither, covered with an antic face,

To fleer and scorn at our solemnity?
Now by the stock and honour of my kin,
To strike him dead I hold it not a sin.

CAPULET: Why, how now, kinsman? wherefore storm you so?

TYBALT: Uncle, this is a Montague, our foe;
A villain that is hither come in spite,
To scorn at our solemnity this night.

CAPULET: Young Romeo is it?

TYBALT: 'Tis he, that villain Romeo.

CAPULET: Content thee, gentle coz, let him alone:
He bears him like a portly gentleman;
And to say truth, Verona brags of him,
To be a virtuous and well-governed youth.
I would not for the wealth of all this town
Here in my house do him disparagement
Therefore be patient, take no note of him:
It is my will: the which if thou respect,
Show a fair presence, and put off these frowns
An ill-beseeming semblance for a feast.

Tybalt, forced to be patient, heeds his uncle's wishes to leave the well-mannered Romeo alone, but vows that

Romeo will pay dearly for his intrusion. Meanwhile, Romeo, unaware that his identity is known approaches the woman who has already made him forget Rosaline.

ROMEO: If I profane with my unworthiest hand
　　This holy shrine, the gentle sin is this,
　　My lips two blushing pilgrims ready stand,
　　To smooth the rough touch with a gentle kiss.

JULIET: Good pilgrim, you do wrong your hand too much,
　　Which mannerly devotion shows in this,
　　For saints have hands that pilgrims' hands do touch,
　　And palm to palm is holy palmers' kiss.

ROMEO: Have not saints lips, and holy palmers too?

JULIET: Ay, pilgrim, lips that they must use in prayer.

ROMEO: O then, dear saint, let lips do what hands do,
　　They pray, grant thou, lest faith turn to despair.

JULIET: Saints do not move though grant for prayers sake.

ROMEO: Then move not while my prayer's effect I take.
　　Thus from my lips, by thine, my sin is purged.

JULIET: Then have my lips the sin that they have took.

ROMEO: Sin from my lips? O trespass sweetly urged!

Give me my sin again!

JULIET: You kiss by the book.

Juliet's nurse calls to her charge that she is wanted by her mother, and with Juliet gone, Romeo asks the nurse who his new-found love is. He learns she is of the dreaded house of Capulet.

NURSE: Marry, bachelor, Her mother is the lady of the house...

ROMEO: Is she a Capulet?
O dear account! my life is my foe's debt.

Juliet, too, despairs when she discovers that the man she has fallen in love with is Romeo and a Montague.

JULIET: My only love sprung from my only hate.
    Too early seen, unknown, and known too late
    Prodigious birth of love it is to me,
    That I must love a loathed enemy.

The feast being at an end, Romeo, Benvolio and
Mercutio leave and begin their journey home. But Romeo
leaves them to return to Capulet's house, climbing into
the orchard behind the house. A few moments later Juliet
unexpectedly appears at an upper window. Romeo
speaks aloud - although Juliet cannot hear him:

Romeo: But soft, what light through yonder window
    breaks?
    It is the east, and Juliet is the sun.
    Arise fair sun, and kill the envious moon,
    Who is already sick and pale with grief
    See how she leans her cheek upon her hand.
    O that I were a glove upon that hand,
    That I might touch that cheek.

Juliet, equally passionate about Romeo, struggles with

the awful truth that he is a Montague, and therefore her enemy. She, too, speaks aloud, unaware of her loved one's presence.

JULIET: O Romeo, Romeo, wherefore art thou Romeo?
    Deny thy father and refuse thy name.
    Or if thou wilt not, be but sworn my love,
    And I'll no longer be a Capulet.

ROMEO: [*Aside*] Shall I hear more, or shall I speak at this?

JULIET: 'Tis but thy name that is my enemy;
    Thou art thyself, though not a Montague.
    What's in a name? That which we call a rose
    By any other name would smell as sweet,
    So Romeo would were he not Romeo called,
    Retain that dear perfection which he owes,
    Without that title, Romeo, doff thy name,
    And for thy name which is no part of thee,
    Take all my self.

ROMEO: I take thee at thy word:
    Call me but love and I'll be now baptised.
    Henceforth I never will be Romeo.

Juliet is initially startled to hear a man speak to her from the orchard, but soon recognizes the voice and addresses him.

JULIET: How cams't thou hither, tell me, and wherefore?
    The orchard walls are high, and hard to climb,
    And the place death, considering who thou art,
    If any of my kinsmen find thee here.

ROMEO: Alack, there lies more peril in thine eye
    Than twenty of their swords. Look thou but sweet
    And I am proof against their enmity.

Juliet is concerned that Romeo may think her too forward, so she assures him that she never would have spoken had she known he could hear her. She asks that he believe she speaks not lightly and that she will be true to him - should he return her love.

JULIET: Thou know'st the mask of night is on my face,
    Else would a maiden blush bepaint my cheek
    For that which thou hadst heard me speak tonight.
    Fain would I dwell on form, fain, fain, deny
    What I have spoke. But farewell, compliment.
    Dost thou love me? I know thou wilt say ay,
    And I will take thy word, yet if thou swearest,
    Thou may prove false: at lover's perjuries
    They say Jove laughs. O, gentle Romeo,
    If thou dost love, pronounce it faithfully.
    Or if thou thinkest I am too quickly won,
    I'll frown and be perverse and say thee nay,
    So thou wilt woo; but else not for the world.

In truth fair Montague I am too fond,
And therefore thou mayst think my behaviour light.
But trust me gentleman, I'll prove more true
Than those that have more cunning to be strange.
I should have been more strangr, I must confess,
But that thou overheard'st, ere I was aware,
My true-love passion. Therefore pardon me,
And not impute this yielding to light love,
Which by dark night hath so discovered.

ROMEO: Lady, by yonder blessed moon I vow,
That tips with silver all these fruit-tree tops -

JULIET: O swear not by the moon, the inconstant moon,
That monthly changes in her circled orb,
Lest thy love prove likewise variable.

ROMEO: What shall I swear by?

JULIET: Do not swear at all:
Or if thou wilt, swear by thy gracious self,
Which is the god of my idolatry,
And I'll believe thee.

The young lovers are interrupted by Juliet's nurse calling to her. Juliet starts to leave, but returns, proclaiming her readiness to marry Romeo.

JULIET: If that thy bent of love be honourable,
   Thy purpose marriage, send me word tomorrow,
   By one that I'll procure to come to thee,
   Where and what time thou wilt perform the rite,
   And all my fortunes at thy foot I'll lay,
   And follow thee, my lord, throughout the world.

   Romeo leaves and Juliet calls him back - it is clear they
yearn to be together. Eventually the couple part, as day is
breaking, having decided to meet the next day and be
married.

JULIET: Good night, good night. Parting is such sweet
      sorrow,
   That I shall say "goodnight" till it be morrow.

ROMEO: Sleep dwell upon thine eyes, peace in thy breast.
   Would I were sleep and peace, so sweet to rest.

   Romeo leaves for the monastery, to find Friar
Lawrence. The Friar is surprised that Romeo is up so

early and guesses that Romeo's love for Rosaline has kept him from sleeping. Romeo tells him of his new love, and the Friar agrees to help. The Friar hopes that the union of the two may help heal the rift between the two families.

ROMEO: Then plainly know my heart's dear love is set
    On the fair daughter of rich Capulet.
    As mine on hers, so hers is set on mine,
    And all combined, save what thou must combine
    By holy marriage. When, and where, and how,
    We met, we wooed, and made exchange of vow,
    I'll tell thee as we pass; but this I pray,
    That thou consent to marry us today.

FRIAR LAWRENCE: Holy Saint Francis, what a change is
      here?
    Is Rosaline that thou didst love so dear
    So soon forsaken?

ROMEO: Thou chid'st me oft for loving Rosaline.

FRIAR LAWRENCE: For doting, not for loving, pupil mine.

ROMEO: I pray thee, chide me not; her I love now
    Doth grace for grace, and love for love allow:
    The other did not so.

FRIAR LAWRENCE: In one respect I'll thy assistant be:

For this alliance may so happy prove,
To turn your household's rancour to pure love.

The jubilant Romeo meets his friends later that day.
They are delighted to see him in such high spirits, though
they do not know the cause.

MERCUTIO: Why is not this better now than groaning for
        love?
    Now art thou sociable, now art thou Romeo.

While Romeo is being teased by his friends, Juliet's
nurse arrives for Romeo's instructions to her mistress.
Romeo instructs her to tell Juliet to go to confession at
Friar Lawrence's where they will meet and be wed.

JULIET: Good even to my ghostly confessor.

FRIAR LAWRENCE: Romeo shall thank thee daughter for us
        both.

JULIET: As much to him, else is his thanks too much.

ROMEO: Ah, Juliet if the measure of thy joy
    Be heaped like mine, and that thy skill be more
    To blazon it, then sweeten with thy breath
    This neighbour air, and let rich music's tongue
    Unfold the imagined happiness that both
    Receive in either by this dear encounter.

JULIET: Conceit, more rich in matter than in words,
Brags of substance, not of ornament.
They are but beggars that can count their worth.
But my true love is grown to such excess,
I cannot sum up sum of half my wealth.

FRIAR LAWRENCE: Come, come with me, and we will make
short work.
For by your leaves, you shall not stay alone,
Till holy church incorporate two in one.

While the wedding ceremony is taking place, Benvolio
and Mercutio are approached by the vengeful Tybalt who
is looking for Romeo. Tybalt challenges Mercutio, whom
he knows to be Romeo's friend.

TYBALT: Mercutio, thou consortest with Romeo.

MERCUTIO: Consort? What dost thou make us minstrels? An thou make minstrels of us, look to hear nothing but discords. Here's my fiddlestick, here's that shall make you dance. [*Points to his sword*] 'Zounds, consort!

Seeing Romeo approaching, Tybalt turns and redirects the challenge. But Romeo, now secretly wed to Tybalt's cousin Juliet, does not want to fight.

TYBALT: Romeo, the love I bear thee can afford
    No better term than this. Thou art a villan.

ROMEO: Tybalt, the reason that I have to love thee
    Doth much excuse the appertaining rage
    To such a greeting. Villain am I none.
    Therefore farewell, I see thou knowst me not.

TYBALT: Boy, this shall not excuse the injuries
    That thou hast done me, therefore turn and draw.

ROMEO: I do protest I never injured thee,
    But love thee better than thou canst devise,
    Till thou shalt know the reason of my love.
    And so good Capulet, which name I tender
    As dearly as my own, be satisfied.

Mercutio is shocked by Romeo professing "love" for Tybalt and takes it upon himself to defend his

friend's honor.

MERCUTIO: Tybalt, you rat-catcher, will you walk?

TYBALT: I am for you.

ROMEO: Gentle Mercutio, put thy rapier up...
   Hold Tybalt. Good Mercutio.

All too quickly, Tybalt turns, lunging at Mercutio under Romeo's arm and wounding him fatally. Tybalt flees, leaving the dying Mercutio and a grieving Romeo.

MERCUTIO: I am hurt. A plague on both your houses, I am
      sped.
   Is he gone and hath nothing?

ROMEO: This gentleman, the Prince's near ally,
   My very friend, hath got this mortal hurt
   In my behalf; my reputation stained
   With Tybalt's slander. Tybalt that an hour
   Hath been my cousin. O sweet Juliet,
   Thy beauty hath made me effeminate,
   And in my temper softened valour's steel.

As Benvolio and Romeo lament brave Mercutio's death, Tybalt returns. A second fight ensues, between Romeo and Tybalt, and Tybalt is killed. Romeo has no choice but to flee or be put to death.

BENVOLIO: Romeo away, be gone.
  The citizens are up, and Tybalt slain.
  Stand not amazed, the Prince will doom thee death,
  If thou art taken. Hence, be gone, away.

Soon a crowd of citizens, including the Lords Capulet and Montague, have gathered. Romeo's mother, Lady Montague, pleads for her child's life. The Prince softens his previous decree; Romeo will not be put to death, but he will be banished.

PRINCE: I will be deaf to pleading and excuses,
  Nor tears nor prayers shall purchase out abuses.
  Therefore use none. Let Romeo hence in haste,
  Else, when he's found that hour is his last.

Juliet, meanwhile, is happily looking forward to seeing Romeo, when her nurse arrives, distraught over Tybalt's death and Romeo's banishment. Juliet is torn between anger against Romeo for killing her cousin Tybalt and relief that Romeo lives, whom Tybalt would have slain.

JULIET: O serpent heart, hid with a flowering face!
  Did ever dragon keep so fair a cave?
  Beautiful tyrant, fiend angelical,
  Dove-feathered raven, wolfish ravening lamb,
  Despised substance of divinest show,
  Just opposite to what thou justly seem'st,

A damned saint, an honourable villain.
O nature, what hadst thou to do in hell,
When thou didst bower the spirit of a fiend
In mortal paradise of such sweet flesh?
Was ever book containing such vile matter
So fairly bound? O that deceit should dwell
In such a gorgeous palace!

Her joy over the fact that Romeo still lives is soon darkened with the fact of his exile.

JULIET: Romeo is banished: to speak that word
Is father, mother, Tybalt, Romeo, Juliet,
All slain, all dead. Romeo is banished,
There is no end, no limit, measure bound,
In that word's death, no words can that woe sound.

Romeo has not yet gone from Verona - but has first taken refuge with Friar Lawrence. It is here he learns of the sentence passed upon him, not death but banishment, which the Friar calls "dear mercy." To Romeo, banishment is not mercy, but torture.

ROMEO: 'Tis torture and not mercy, heaven is here
　　Where Juliet lives, and every cat and dog,
　　And little mouse, every unworthy thing
　　Live here in heaven, and may look on her,
　　But Romeo may not.

Juliet's nurse, having guessed where Romeo would hide himself, arrives with a message from her lady.

ROMEO: Speakst thou of Juliet? How is it with her?

NURSE: Oh, she says nothing sir, but weeps and weeps,
　　And now falls on her head, and starts up,
　　And Tybalt calls, and then on Romeo cries,
　　And then falls down again.

The Friar suggests a plan - Romeo will visit Juliet secretly to say goodbye, and then go to Mantua and wait for the Friar to announce the marriage to all.

FRIAR LAWRENCE: Go get thee to thy love as was decreed,
　　Ascend her chamber hence and comfort her.

But look thou stay not till the watch be set,
For then thou shalt live till we can find a time
To blazon your marriage, reconcile your friends,
Beg pardon of the Prince, and call thee back,
With twenty hundred thousand times more joy.

Meanwhile, unaware of his daughter's marriage, Lord Capulet is approached by Paris, a noble youth, for Juliet's hand in marriage. The lord gives his consent and a date is set for the wedding.

CAPULET: What say you to Thursday?

PARIS: My lord, I would that Thursday were tomorrow.

CAPULET: Well get you gone; a' Thursday be it then.
    Go you to Juliet ere you go to bed,
    Prepare her, wife, against this wedding day.

Juliet's father does not know that in Juliet's chamber, the newly-wed couple are spending their first night together. It seems to Juliet that the night passes too quickly, and anxious to delay her husband's departure, she tells

34

him it is still night and not morning yet.

JULIET: Wilt thou be gone? It is not yet near day,
 It was the nightingale and not the lark,
 That pierced the fearful hollow of thine ear;
 Nightly she sings on yon pomegranate tree.
 Believe me love, it was the nightingale.

ROMEO: It was the lark, the herald of the morn,
 No nightingale. Look, love, what envious streaks
 Do lace the severing clouds in yonder East:
 Night's candles are burnt out, and jocund day
 Stands tiptoe on the misty mountain tops.
 I must be gone and live, or stay and die.

 Shortly after Romeo leaves, Lady Capulet comes to her daughter's room and tells Juliet of Lord Capulet's decision to allow Paris to marry her.

JULIET: I will not marry yet, and when I do, I swear
 It shall be Romeo, whom you know I hate,
 Rather than Paris.

 Lord Capulet is deaf to all Juliet's pleadings and declares that she will marry Paris even if he has to drag Juliet to the church.

CAPULET: Mistress minion you,

Thank me no thanklings, nor proud me no prouds,
But fettle your fine joints against Thursday next,
To go with Paris to Saint Peter's Church,
Or I will drag thee on a hurdle thither.

Juliet turns to her nurse for comfort, but the nurse advises Juliet to forget Romeo and marry Paris. Resolving to confide no more in the nurse, Juliet decides to visit Friar Lawrence and seek his help.

JULIET: Ancient damnation! O most wicked fiend!
Is it more sin to wish me thus forsworn,
Or to dispraise my lord with that same tongue
Which she hath praised him with above compare
So many thousand times? Go counsellor;
Thou and my bosom henceforth shall be twain.
I'll to the friar to know his remedy.
If all else fail, myself have the power to die.

When Juliet arrives at Friar Lawrence's he tells her he has already heard of her impending marriage and consoles her. Juliet says she will kill herself if she cannot avoid the marriage.

JULIET: Tell me not friar, that thou hearest of this,
Unless thou tell me how I may prevent it.
If in thy wisdom thou canst give no help,
Do thou but call my resolution wise,

And with this knife I'll help it presently.
God joined my heart and Romeo's, thou our hands;
And ere this hand, by thee to Romeo's sealed,
Shall be the label to another deed,
Or my true heart with treacherous revolt
Turn to another, this shall slay them both.

Recognizing the strength of Juliet's resolve to kill herself if necessary, the good friar proposes another plan.

FRIAR LAWRENCE: If, rather than marry County Paris,
    Thou hast the strength of will to slay thyself,
    Then it is likely thou wilt undertake
    A thing like death to chide away this shame,
    That cop'st with death himself to escape from it;
    And if thou darest, I'll give thee remedy.

JULIET: O bid me leap, rather than marry Paris,
    From off the battlements of any tower;
    And I will do it without fear or doubt,
    To live an unstained wife to my sweet love.

Friar Lawrence gives Juliet a vial of sleeping potion and instructs her to take it the following night. The potion will make it appear that Juliet is dead and the Friar knows that she will then be taken to the family vault. The Friar will arrange to be there with Romeo when she awakes. Juliet agrees to the Friar's plan.

FRIAR LAWRENCE: Hold then, go home, be merry, give
      consent
  To marry Paris. Wednesday is tomorrow;
  Tomorrow night look that thou lie alone,
  Let not the nurse lie with thee in thy chamber.
  Take thou this vial, being then in bed,
  And this distilling liquor drink thou off;
  When presently through all thy veins shall run
  A cold and drowsy humour; for no pulse
  Shall keep his native progress, but surcease...
  Now when the bridegroom in the morning comes
  To rouse thee from thy bed, there art thou dead.
  Then as the manner of our country is,
  In thy best robes uncovered on the bier,
  Thou shalt be borne to that same ancient vault,
  Where all the kindred of the Capulets lie.

In the meantime, against thou shalt awake,
Shall Romeo by my letters know our drift,
And hither shall he come; and he and I
Will watch thy waking, and that very night
Shall Romeo bear thee hence to Mantua.

JULIET. Give me, give me. O tell not me of fear.

Now, according to the plan, Juliet returns home and
apologizes for her disobedience. Lord Capulet is delighted with this change in his headstrong daughter and
decides the wedding shall take place the next day. Juliet
retires to her chamber and prepares to take the potion,
but first she contemplates the things that can go wrong.
Nevertheless, she soon finds the courage to take the
potion.

JULIET. Come vial. What if this mixture do not work at all?
Shall I be married then tomorrow morning?
No, no, this shall forbid it. Lie thou there.[*Lays down a*
dagger]
What if it be a poison which the friar
Subtly hath ministered to have me dead,
Lest in this marriage he should be dishonoured,
Because he married me before to Romeo?
I fear it is, and yet methinks it should not,
For he hath still been tried a holy man.
How if when I am laid in the tomb,

I wake before the time that Romeo
Come to redeem me? there's a fearful point.
Shall I not then be stifled in the vault,
To whose foul mouth no healthsome air breathes in,
And there die strangled ere my Romeo comes?...
O if I wake, shall I not be distraught,
Environed with all these hideous fears,
And madly play with my forefathers,
joints, And pluck the mangled Tybalt from his shroud,
And in this rage with some great kinsman's bone,
As with a club, dash out my desperate brains?
O look methinks I see my cousin's ghost
Seeking out Romeo that did spit his body
Upon a rapier's point - stay Tybalt stay!
Romeo! Romeo! Romeo! I drink to thee.

The next morning, Paris arrives with Friar Lawrence to escort his intended bride to the altar. The nurse is sent to wake Juliet and discovers her charge laid on the bed dressed for her wedding and, to all appearances, dead. The wedding ceremony is now replaced by Juliet's funeral. The words of both the Friar and Lord Capulet are charged with irony and yet darkly ominous.

FRIAR LAWRENCE: Come is the bride ready to go to church?

CAPULET: Ready to go, but never to return.
    O son, the night before thy wedding-day

Hath death lain with thy wife; there she lies,
Flower that she was, deflowered by him...

FRIAR LAWRENCE: Dry up your tears, and stick your
        rosemary
    On this fair corpse; and as the custom is,
    All in her best array bear her to church.

CAPULET: Sir, go you in, and madam, go with him;
    And go Sir Paris; every one prepare
    To follow this fair corpse unto her grave.

Romeo, unaware of the recent turn of events, waits in
eager anticipation for a letter or message from Juliet.
When he sees his servant Balthasar approach he hurries
to meet him. Unaware of the plan, Balthasar tells Romeo
what has happened.

ROMEO: News from Verona. How now Balthasar,
    Dost thou not bring me letters from the friar?
    How doth my lady? Is my father well?
    How doth my Juliet? That I ask again,
    For nothing can be ill if she be well.

BALTHASAR: Her body sleeps in Capel's monument,
    And her immortal part with angels lives.
    I saw her laid low in her kindred's vault,
    And presently took post to tell it you.

Grief-stricken at the news of Juliet's death, Romeo looks for a means of ending his own life so that he can join his beloved in death. Romeo goes to an apothecary's shop and buys a poison. He goes to Juliet's tomb, planning to take the poison so he can lie beside his wife for eternity.

ROMEO: Hold, there is forty ducats, let me have
   A dram of poison, such soon-speeding gear
   As will disperse itself though all the veins,
   That the life-weary taker may fall dead ...

APOTHECARY: Put this in any liquid thing you will
   And drink it off, and if you had the strength
   Of twenty men, it would dispatch you straight.

Back in Verona, Friar Lawrence meets a fellow monk,

Friar John, to whom he had entrusted his important letter to Romeo telling of Juliet's feigned death and instructing Romeo to come to her. Friar John explains that he was unable to visit Mantua and deliver the letter. Alarmed by this news, Friar Lawrence rushes to Juliet's tomb so that she will not wake alone in that dreadful place. He will then write to Romeo again, and in the meantime keep Juliet with him until Romeo arrives to take her to Mantua.

FRIAR LAWRENCE: Now must I to the monument alone;
    Within this three hours will fair Juliet wake.
    She will beshrew me much that Romeo
    Hath had no notice of these accidents.
    But I will write again to Mantua,
    And keep her at my cell till Romeo come.

Paris, meanwhile, makes his way to Juliet's grave. While he is laying flowers at her tomb, he sees Romeo carrying a crowbar. Paris thinks that Romeo has come to desecrate the grave and therefore accosts him. In the fight that follows, Paris is killed. Paris's page runs for help.

PARIS: Stop thy unhallowed toil, vile Montague.
    Can vengeance be pursued further than death?
    Condemned villain, I do apprehend thee.
    Obey and go with me, for thou must die.

ROMEO: I must indeed, and therefore came I hither.

Good gentle youth, tempt not a desperate man; ...
By urging me to fury. O be gone.

PARIS: I do defy thy conjuration,
And apprehend thee for a felon here.

ROMEO: Wilt thou provoke me? Then have at thee boy.

PAGE: O Lord they fight! I will go call the watch.

PARIS: O I am slain. If thou be merciful,
Open the tomb, lay me with Juliet.

At this point Romeo realizes that the man he has just
killed is Paris, a relative of Romeo's dead friend, Mercutio,
and the man Juliet was to have married. As a tribute,
Romeo lays Paris's body inside the tomb near Juliet.
Heartbroken, Romeo addresses his wife, still beautiful in
death.

ROMEO: O my love, my wife!
Death that hath sucked the honey of thy breath,

Hath had no power yet upon they beauty.
Thou art not conquered; beauty's ensign yet
Is crimson in thy lips and in thy cheeks,
And death's pale flag is not advanced there...
Why are thou yet so fair? Shall I believe
That insubstantial death is amorous,
And that the lean abhorred monster keeps
Thee here in dark to be his paramour?
For fear of that, I still will stay with thee,
And never from this palace of dim night
Depart again. Here, here will I remain
With worms that are everlasting rest;
And shake the yoke of inauspicious stars
From this world-wearied flesh.Eyes look your last.
Arms, take your last embrace. And lips, O you
The doors of breath, seal with a righteous kiss
A dateless bargain to engrossing death...
Here's to my love! [*Drinks*] O true apothecary!
Thy drugs are quick. Thus with a kiss I die.

Friar Lawrence arrives upon the unhappy scene, seeing first the bloody swords at the mouth of the tomb. He enters the vault and sees the bodies of Paris and Romeo, and then Juliet begins to wake.

FRIAR LAWRENCE: What mean these masterless and gory
    swords

To lie discoloured by this place of peace?
Romeo! O pale! Who else! What, Paris too?
And steeped in blood? Ah what an unkind hour
Is guilty of this lamentable chance!
The lady stirs.

JULIET: O comfortable friar, where is my lord?
I do well remember well where I should be,
And there I am. Where is my Romeo?

The friar must now tell Juliet the sad news that Romeo
has committed suicide beside her. The Friar's plan to help
the young lovers has yielded only sorrow and death.
Fearing the consequences, the Friar urges Juliet to leave
with him.

FRIAR LAWRENCE: A greater power than we can contradict
Hath thwarted our intents. Come, come away.
Thy husband in thy bosom there lies dead;
And Paris too. Come I'll dispose of thee
Among a sisterhood of holy nuns.
Stay not to question, for the watch is coming.
Come, go good Juliet, I dare no longer stay.

JULIET: Go, get thee hence, for I will not away.
What's here? A cup closed in my true love's hand?
Poison I see hath been his timeless end.
O churl, drunk all, and left no friendly drop

To help me after? I will kiss thy lips;
Haply some poison yet doth hang on them,
To make me die with a restorative.
Thy lips are warm.

WATCH: [*Outside*] Lead boy, which way?

JULIET: Yea, noise? Then I'll be brief. O happy dagger!
This is thy sheath; there rest and let me die. [*stabs herself*]

The watchman, finding Romeo's servant, Balthasar, and Friar Lawrence hiding in the graveyard, detains them until the Prince arrives. Friar Lawrence is then ordered to explain the grisly sight. He relates the sad tale of the star-crossed lovers to those assembled. A letter that Romeo has given his servant Balthasar confirms the friar's story. The Prince turns to the assembled Montagues and Capulets, whose hateful feud has now been punished. He feels guilty for ignoring the situation and says he has lost two relatives as a result - Mercutio and Paris.

PRINCE: This letter doth make good the friar's words,
Their course of love, the tidings of her death.
And here he writes that he did buy a poison
Of a poor apothecary, and therewithal
Came to this vault to die and lie with Juliet.
Where be these enemies? Capulet, Montague,

See what a scourge is laid upon your hate,
That heaven finds a means to kill your joys with love.
And I for winking at your discords too
Have lost a brace of kinsmen; all are punished.

Brought together by their shared grief, the Lords
Capulet and Montague at last shake hands, calling an end
to their feud. Lord Montague promises to raise a statue to
his ill-fated daughter-in-law, Juliet, as a tribute to her
steadfast love and faithfulness.

CAPULET: O brother Montague, give me thy hand.
This is my daughter's jointure, for no more
Can I demand.

MONTAGUE: But I can give thee more.
For I will raise her statue in pure gold,

That while Verona by that name is known,
There shall no figure at such rate be set
As that of true and faithful Juliet.

CAPULET: As rich shall Romeo by his lady lie,
Poor sacrifices of our enmity.

Finally, the Prince disperses the crowd and reflects on the sad events that have caused even the sun to hide in sorrow.

PRINCE: A glooming peace this morning with it brings;
The sun for sorrow will not show his head.
Go hence to have more talk of these sad things;
Some shall be pardoned, and some punished.
For never was a story of more woe
Than this of Juliet and her Romeo.

mistempered: forged for an evil purpose

cankered: rusted or rotten

Ethiop's: Ethiopian's

rude: rough or unmannerly

antic face: a mask

fleer: mock or sneer

coz: relation

portly: dignified and well-mannered

disparagement: dishonor or shame

prodigious: unnatural

wherefore: why

fain: gladly

strange: distant

rancour: hate

blazon: proclaim

donsortest: to accompany or be friends with

consort: a servant

mistress minion: headstrong child

fettle: prepare or groom

chide: drive or scold

surcease: cease

tried: proved

healthsome: pure and fresh

strangled: suffocated

conceit: thought

green: new or fresh

apothecary: druggist or chemist

ducats: gold coins

brace: pair

jointure: the estate which the bridegroom endowed his wife